ANCHOR
BOOKS

DREAMS OF FOREVER

Edited by

Simon Harwin

First published in Great Britain in 2003 by
ANCHOR BOOKS
Remus House,
Coltsfoot Drive,
Peterborough, PE2 9JX
Telephone (01733) 898102

SB ISBN 1 84418 246 0

FOREWORD

Anchor Books is a small press, established in 1992, with the aim of promoting readable poetry to as wide an audience as possible.

We hope to establish an outlet for writers of poetry who may have struggled to see their work in print.

The poems presented here have been selected from many entries, and as always editing proved to be a difficult task.

I trust this selection will delight and please the authors and all those who enjoy reading poetry.

Simon Harwin
Editor

CONTENTS

BUBBLES

(For Jude & India)

Bubbles are amazing
There are many to be found,
Big bubbles, small bubbles,
Clear, delicate and round.

Bubbles from a soap bar
On a flannel as you scrub,
Perfumed bubbles from the foam
Swelling softly in the tub.

Tiny bubbles, sparkling bubbles,
Squashed inside a straw,
Madly floating in lemonade,
Escaping as you pour.

Freshly formed, neat bubbles,
In puddles on the ground,
Resting on the rainwater
Just waiting to be found.

Children in a paddling pool
Blowing bubbles from a pot,
Milky bubbles blown from babies
Lying in their cot.

Sticky bubbles, the biggest bubbles,
From bubblegum that's pink,
And dishwater dirty bubbles
Dissolving in the sink.

Nearly all, they keep on floating
Up and up, they never stop.
But the bubble I like best
Is the bubble that goes . . . *pop!*

Louise Mawbey

SNOWBOUND

I thought I heard
A pussy cat
Mew in the driven snow
He uttered not a single word
The pussy cat
Where could he go?

He stalked me
The pussy cat
His paw marks in a row
There you see
The pussy cat
Trapped in the driven snow.

There he is
The pussy cat
His jaw is blue with cold
The land was his
Just where he sat
A pussy cat so bold.

Too bold he was
The pussy cat
Caught out in the snow
He couldn't pass
The pussy cat
Tho' walking to and fro.

Angus Richmond

HAUNT AWAY

Darkness House is a chilling place to be
Where ghosts will scare and haunt with glee.
The creepy pictures with eyes that roam
Make all visitors scream and run for home.

This eerie house on top of the hill
Was never left in someone's will.
It's for the spirits, evil or good.
Visit it children - you never should!

The kids who go there just to play,
Come home nervous, never to say
What they heard or even saw
The fright they had so painfully raw.

A shadow, Darkness House throws down
Over the people who live in its town.
The adults know and stay well away,
But children dare each other up that way.

Their characters so full of devil may care,
Make them curious and unaware
Of the unknown that lurks and looms
In all of Darkness House's rooms!

Some children never return at all
And parents search as night does fall.
But they won't be found, forever missing
Amongst the ghosts and their haunting hissing.

Children - to Darkness House - do not fare,
It's not brave - it's a deadly dare.
The ghouls in there - so it's said,
Are looking for new souls to join their living dead!

Enfys Evans

A BIT TOO MAGIC

There's a dragon in that sea cave!
    when a wave goes in, he'll roar.
Silly dragon! If you don't like
    water, get yourself a door!

Here, an elf lives in a tree trunk,
    one who's got an aching tooth,
When the wind blows, he starts groaning,
    listen! I'm telling the truth.

Near the stream a fairy's playing
    on a set of little bells,
Like the ones at school - but tiny,
    where she is though, no one tells!

There's a *big* snake in the heather,
    (Daddy thinks they're only small),
I can hear how loud he rustles
    when the hov'ring skylarks call!

In the cornfield seas roll dryly,
    just look at the way they move!
Rippling like the waves we play in,
    it's the same - my case I prove.

But there's something I *can't* work out!
    when the sun sets in the sea,
Why is there no steam or boiling . . .
    this one *really* puzzles me!

Funny how the grown-ups never
    seem to see these things I do,
Maybe they're a bit too magic
    for most grown-ups - how 'bout you?

David J C Wheeler

UNDER MY BED

There is something living under my bed,
A great big hairy monster
With a great big scary head.

Wanting to bite me, waiting for a chance,
When I go upstairs at night
So I don't allow him a glance.

For if he catches sight of me,
His dinner menu I will be.

I leap onto my bed from far away,
So that hidden in the darkness
Is where he must stay.

Never dangle limbs over the edge,
For he is a carnivore
Who does not like veg.

If he grabs hold of me,
His dinner menu I might be.

Long, sharp, pointy teeth, I think,
A great big mouth and red eyes,
He moves as quickly as a blink.

Once in bed I am quite safe from him,
He's not allowed to come out
And climb up, to pull me in.

His dinner menu I will not be,
So I keep a hard shoe next to me.

P S D MacArthur

A BAD DAY!

Today has been the kind of day
You wish had simply gone away
Before the sun rose in the east.
Of misery there's been a feast!

On getting up I stubbed my toe,
My trouser zip got stuck, although
Sour milk on cereals was a pain,
As bad, at least, as heavy rain.

My tyre went flat, the chain worked loose,
My old bike wasn't any use;
I got to lessons late and wet,
My teacher got into a pet.

She kept me in from twelve to one
Because my homework wasn't done.
The soccer board was far from Heaven -
They'd dropped me from the First Eleven!

A football kicked into our neighbour's
Did not do his greenhouse favours -
My pocket money stopped until
It cleared the glazier's hefty bill.

A missing gerbil caused a frown;
My burnt toast landed jam-side down.
A bad egg made an awful pong;
My Air-Fix model went all wrong.

My midnight reading was a freak;
The torch's batteries are weak.
A day like this would make you weep,
I hope to blot it out in sleep!

Philip Worth

A RAINBOW

a display of seven colours
violet, indigo, blue, green, yellow, orange and red
an arch in the sky, like the bow of a clown
the sun's rays reflecting through rain or mist
a happy frown

Mairead Macbeath

PEA-NUT

Said Jamie, 'Mum! It would appear
I've stuffed a green pea in my ear.
I've tried but cannot get it out,
Don't tell me off, don't scream and shout.
Can you blow in my other ear?
There's nothing in between, I fear;
If not, perhaps a thump, I judge,
Around the ear, will make it budge.
Perhaps if you would shake me hard
You'll catch the pea right off its guard,
And from my earhole it will drop,
Or whiz with a resounding pop.
Please try - evacuate this pea,
Don't let it germinate in me.'

His mother said, 'It does seem odd,
We're so alike - peas in a pod,
But I would never thrust a pulse
Into my ear, I would convulse.
The very thought makes me turn green,
You could have tried a runner bean!
Come here. My! What a lot of wax,
I'll have to give you hefty whacks
To each side of your head, in turn,
Don't tell me that your ears both burn.
It's sad that we have come to blows,
Thank God! It's not stuck up your nose!'
No matter what she did or tried,
The pea remained stuck fast inside.

So, to the doctor's they both went
With pea extraction their intent.
The doctor, with a stifled grin,
Grabbed Jamie's ear and looked right in.

His auriscope confirmed his fears,
Two pea-sized spheres between the ears,
But which was brain and which was pea?
It was so very hard to see.
So, 'Eeny, meeny, miney, mo,'
He said, 'I'll guess I'll have a go.'
With tweezers, he probed with glee,
By luck, he pulled the garden pea.
Since then, poor Jamie has complained
That people say that he's pea-brained.

Jax Burgess

IMAGINATION

In my house
That's inside my head
Where buttercups grow
And fly instead
The grass yellow
The trees are blue
No one is known by
Me, I and you
Your next door neighbour is always smiling
Frowning is against the law
Everyone's door is always open
For everyone to enjoy and explore
The stars they're not needed
Neither is the sun
The moon has packed up its things
For my world has just begun!

Emma Scott

FREDDIE FROG

amphibian family ranidae
fish-like tadpoles dart and play
gradually losing gill slits and tail
metamorphosed frog-thumbnail

one in particular to our small pond arrived
leaped into quick and to the bottom dived
to us spectators so friendly, tame
we thought Freddie could be his name

we never knew how he found our place
each year making it his summer base
mornings sleeping 'neath the reeds
after lunch siesta through sun-blazed weeds

by night, dining on our slugs and snails
at dawn, return back without fail
as late summer drew to its close
hibernating nearby in dormant pose.

Brian Strand

NOAH'S ANIMAL ANTICS
(For my grandchildren with lots of love from Nanny Audrey Harman)

When the Artful Angry Adder Asked the Address of the Ark,
the Boring Bashful Badger only knew it in the dark.
The Crafty Clicking Cricket Caught a lift on a Creaking Cart,
but the Docile Dawdling Donkey was left Dreaming at the start.
The Ever Eyeful Eagle Escaped Easily from the ledge,
the Fluffy Fluttering Finches Flew out Fast From in the hedge.
The Grouchy Gruffy Goats were left Gnawing at the Gate,
while the Heavy Humping Hippos Had a Habit of being late.
The Itchy Irksome Insects hitched a ride on an Ibis's back,
while the Jolly Joking Jellyfish Just drifted on a wreck.
The Kindly little Koala with a face that you could kiss,
Leapt up onto the Leopard's back whose Lips you couldn't miss.
The Multi-legged Millipede Meandered through the Mud,
to where the Naughty Newts were stuck and had to have a tug.
The Ostrich Overtook the lot by taking massive strides,
but the Podgy Prickly Porcupine Proposed to take his time.
The Quail was asking Questions - 'Whose holding up the Queue?'
it's the Rumbling Robust Rhino who takes up the space of two.
The Sloppy Sliding Sealion had no legs to take the Strain,
but caught up the Trundling Tortoise who took his Tent
for when it rained.
The Weary Wobbling Walrus Was left Wondering What to do
with all the eXcess animals still waiting at the zoo.
The Yak began to Yawn for he was bored with all the Yelling,
but the Zebra Zipped up his stripy suit and was ready to get going.

All the animals made it to the ark with plenty of time to spare
and when the rain began to fall they were glad they all got there.

Audrey Harman

HARRY WHO

Harry Who shouted, 'Boo,'
And gave himself a fright,
Poor little Harry
Couldn't get to sleep that night.

Harry Who skipped to school
Wee Harry was no fool,
Missed his skip, made him trip
And landed in a pool.

Harry Who was no jackass
As he sat in his class,
Counting up his sums by ten
Getting them wrong now and then.

Harry Who got in a stew
At the dinner bell,
Dropped his plate of mash
Oh heck, oh damn, oh well!

Harry Who was having fun
Thought that he could run,
Deary me, hit a tree,
Now he's lying in the sun.

J Lanigan

MONA

What was it producing that loud din in the night,
Certainly caused a fuss, gave Mona a huge fright.
'Not sleeping in my room again,' Mona declared,
'Won't,' she said, no matter how much her brother glared.

'Wind was howling,' Bob said, 'that silly thing was all
I heard bricks rolling down the outer kitchen wall.'
'No! No!' said Mona. 'It was much, much more than that,'
And went into the garden to find her black cat.

Stroking Matilda lovingly in the spare bedroom,
Mona thought hard and long as she gave cat a groom.
In her own room she crept up to the windowpane,
'It's a branch hitting the glass again and again.'

Eventide and outside it had begun to rain,
Noise Mona previously heard began again.
But now she was no longer scared but reassured,
'That branch,' she said, while cuddling the cat she adored.

S Mullinger

ENCHANTMENTS

sorcery, wizardry, witchcraft and magic spells,
dungeons, darkly deep, and deep unfathomable wells,
goblins, demons, devils, sprites and little elves,
fairy tales and legends, stacked cobwebbed on dusty shelves.
covens of witches prancing around their steaming brews,
cackling, croaking, chanting in those ghastly creaking shoes.
none of this enchants me, nor could ever be as serene
as the sweet enchantment of beauty, when first seen.

Stewart Gordon

THE TORTOISE

The tortoise said, 'I know I'm slow,
But there is nowhere that I need to go,
For I carry my house around with me
And wherever I am, I'm home you see.
So I am never in a rush,
It may take me hours to round a bush.
And just to go from here to there
Might take me days, but I don't care,
For I'm quite content, you must believe,
So here I'll stay, until I leave.'

Thomas R Slater

HARRY WHO?

I'm told I'm a child
And must do
What children do
I'm told I'm a teenager
And difficult to manage
I'm told I'm old
And must do as I'm told
I'm always told what to be
When am I going to be me?

P Ismail

OVER THE MOON

Over the moon and far away in the land
Of the laughing cow, we packed our bags and
Took a trip on the back of a giant snail.
Higher and higher above the rooftops until we
Almost touched the sky, then we came to rest on
A mountain top made of apple pie.
On and on we travelled across the rivers wide,
Until the giant snail said, 'I must rest now,
I'm feeling rather tired.'
So we landed on an island across the seven seas,
Where crocodiles and spiders grew bigger than the trees.
We drank the milk from coconuts and rested on the sand,
Until Snail said, 'Come on children,
We'll find somewhere else to land.'
We said goodbye to the animals and they waved us on our way,
By now the sun was going down and
The clouds looked dark and grey.
'I think it's time to go back home,' said our friend,
The giant snail, 'I'm going to fly much faster now,
So hold tightly on my tail.'
We whizzed across the tree tops, we could hardly
Catch our breath, hoping we'd be home for tea
Before there was nothing left.
Then all at once in the light of the moon,
Our chimney top came into sight, Snail began to slow
Down now, he gave us such a fright.
'I'll drop you on your roof,' he said, 'for I have many
Miles to fly, I hope you had a pleasant trip
And now I'll say goodbye.'

Elizabeth Woonton

A HORSE CALLED TINY

The boy was sitting on the fence
Staring at the horse,
He'd love to ride it round and round,
But he would have to ask, of course.

The boy stared at the man and asked,
'Is that your horse I see?'
The man smiled down at the little boy,
'Yes, he belongs to me.'

'What's his name?' the boy enquired.
'It's Tiny,' he was told.
A funny name for a great big horse,
Who's big and strong and bold.

'Can I sit upon his back?'
The boy asked hopefully.
'I guess it wouldn't hurt this once,
But you must go carefully.'

The man lifted the boy in place.
It seemed a long way from the ground,
The horse began to stamp his feet,
The boy began to frown.

He didn't like it way up here,
He was afraid that he would fall.
'Please Mr, would you lift me down?
This isn't fun at all.'

W A Ronayne

THE NORRISES

Maurice and Doris Norris
Had a Dalmatian called Boris,
All white with black spots,
Maurice would join up the dots,
Which vexed his poor wife, Doris.

Maurice and Doris Norris
Also had a cat called Horace;
So the daft pair of pets
Were registered at the vets'
As Boris and Horace Norris!

Kathy Rawstron

A TALE OF TAILS

A tale I could tell
Of grey tails.
My garden sprouts tails
Everywhere.
High up on the fence
One is waving,
In circles and circles
It twirls.
Another suspends from a branch
And one from the bird table hangs.
I just catch a glimpse
Of grey fur
As a tail whisks from view
'Midst the flowers.
One day I may see
These elusive
Mysterious owners
So shy,
Who love nuts and bird seed
For food
And seem to spend hours
Digging holes.
Have you guessed who they are?
Yes, you're right!
They're the beady-eyed dwellers
In trees,
The agile and furry
Grey squirrels.

Roma Davies

PUSS, PUSS

Pussy Wallah loves to wallow
Underneath the pussy-willow.

Pussy pauses in her wallow,
Puss pursues some flighty fleases.
Pussy pauses, pussy listens;
Pussy hears a little rustle.
Is it mouses? Pussy pounces;
Misses mouses, snuffles, sneezes.

Pussy combs her wayward whiskers,
Combing them with pussy clawses.
Puss well pleased with pussy whiskers;
White and wiry; pussy proud of.

Pussy pauses in her combing,
Hears a voice call, 'Pussy Wallah,
Pussy, Pussy, here's your supper.
Pussy Wallah,' calls her missus,
'Pussy Wallah, leave your wallow,
Pussy, come and eat your Whiskas.'
Whiskers twitch at scent of Whiskas.
Pussy gobbles up her supper,
Purrs her thanks to Pussy's missus.

Pussy, plump and groomed and purring,
Now returns to pussy-willow
Not to wallow, but to settle,
Fed and flealess, placid, peaceful,
Now to sleep and dream of mouses.

Lovely life, oh Pussy Wallah!

F Jones

DON QUIXOTE

The world is often different
Than the way it appears
As if our mind distorts
What it sees and hears.

Windmills become monsters
Friends become foe
Stories of laughter become
Tales filled with woe.

For we give different meanings
To the words people use
As if we're deceived
By malevolent mews.

A prince can seem a pauper
A beggar in rags
While princesses transform
Into hideous old hags.

And the objects of our desire
Are never what they seem
Because we cover them in fool's gold
And give them an artificial gleam.

So always heed the words
Of any Sancho Panza
Because we can all put on rusty armour
And be men of La Mancha.

Carl Gravestock

SEEING IS BELIEVING?

Take a moment out
to listen to only you,
block out all the noise
and ban distractions too.

Sit alone and think
of things you have been told,
about fairies, elves and unicorns
from the youngest and the old.

You are told it's only fantasy
and none of these exist,
'It's all a load of nonsense,'
the sceptics do insist.

But things have to start somewhere
so where did it all begin?
And the answer, I can tell you,
will only come from within.

Because if you only think
that sight and sound is proof,
then that will be the case
and you will remain aloof.

But if you let your heart decide
what is real and what is not,
instead of feeling negative
things then will change a lot.

Imagine there is a fairy
sitting afoot your bed,
with starry eyes all glistening
with a flower hat on her head.

She smiles at you like something
you have never seen before,
and you get a happy feeling
as your emotions begin to soar.

And as you continue looking
a vision will appear,
because 'believing is seeing,'
as you bring your imaginations near.

So now go and tell the sceptics
that fantasy is there to find,
with a mind's eye and believing
unless they prefer to stay blind!

Kriss Simone

HAPPY BIRTHDAY JOHN

Hello, young John
Happy birthday today
May your wishes come true
In a nice kind of way
You say you can fix it
And try to help Dad
You do your best
And that can't be bad
So just keep on trying
And never give in
Time is on your side
And one day you'll win
Once again best wishes
A day full of joy
We send lots of love
To a great little boy.

Barbara Harrison

THE MOUSE

I'm tiny and my name is Mouse,
You'll often find me in your house,
I'm quiet so you'll often be
Totally unaware of me,
But in the cupboards you will find
The droppings I have left behind,
I'll often nibble food through the pack,
So beware, better watch your back.

Gigglepuss

THE JOKER

He laughs and laughs and laughs all day,
he chuckles and chortles in a hilarious way.
He makes the King and Queen laugh too,
when he tells funny stories that aren't really true.

He wears a bright and special suit
and in it he looks very cute!
He's good at juggling and falling down,
he sings like an angel and looks like a clown.

Wherever the jolly jester goes,
everyone and everybody knows,
because of the sound his little bells make,
the jester man, you can't forsake!

Jessica May White

THE WORLD, IT RUNS ON LOVE

Although sometimes it seems to me
This old world is full of hate,
I know from deep within myself
What makes it tick is love.

And though sometimes it seems to me
That hate triumphs and cancels love
When conflicts rage throughout the world
It's hard then, to believe in love.

But love it is that moves us all
To stand against injustice,
To rage against the powers that are
Allowing this to happen.

The love of God within us all
Provokes us into anger
When we see defenceless souls
Downtrodden, raped and spat upon.

If it were not for that love,
The world and all mankind
Would long ago have ceased to live.
Thank God it runs on love!

Opal Innsbruk

RAINBOW BRIDGES AND FAIRY TALES

Rainbow bridges and fairy tales,
Fleets of galleons with moonlit sails,
Great battles, which rage between men and dragons,
The crackling of flaming arrows which assail the air,
And the care the young prince takes,
When he bids the sweet maid to awake,
Seemingly asleep on the mossy ground,
Which only his kiss will see her rouse.
How did these folk tales come about?
It's so easy to achieve, my friend.
They arose as we dozed, on some winter's night,
As we in contentment toasted out toes,
Or whilst asleep in a slumber deep
And stirred to life, such magic made,
Borne heavenwards into a starry night.
We see as Santa's reindeer race
On their yearly chase around the world,
As children in their sleep, in anticipation stir,
To swear next morn, sleight bells they heard.

At midnight on a warm Midsummer Eve,
As our imagination catches the breeze,
We perceive the arrival of the fairy queen,
With her entourage, as they proceed
To dance in the moon shadows
In some ferny dell, beneath the trees.
To all those worthy, worldly folk,
Who treat the fay realm as a joke,
I ask in all innocence, just believe.

Jonathan Pegg

THE RUMBLEBEE

The rumblebee got on at Baker Street.
He dipped and dived and fuzzed along the train.
The strangers started laughing at his game.
He soared up high, then dropped to buzz their feet,
Then rose once more just like a tiny plane.
The rumblebee got on at Baker Street.
He hovered past my knees then took a seat,
He wasn't really keen on stinging pain,
Just waiting for his stop at Chancery Lane.
The rumblebee got on at Baker Street.

Barry Woods

VE TAIL OF A VEREE CLEVVA GURLL

i haV nEVa LerrnT Two REEd
aZ i Hav NevVa Ceen
ve need

i Kan noTT coWnT Two frEEe
UnlEs yor HELLpin mEe

But i KanN spEL
Reelee wEL
AZZ i amm sHoor Use
KaNn tel!

Goud wurrk, Joolie!
Sum goud spelins and luvly ryttin!

Missez Smiff

Jonathan M Everingham

APRIL RAINBOW

April eyebrow arched in sky
Golden teardrops heaven sent came
Shed by rainbow's downcast eye
To rest on flower petals same
As dewdrops, in the morn, that glint
Velvet fronds resting pearls divine
Seems rainbow's luminesce tint
Holds earth and sky in shimmering line
'Make a wish.'
Children of early dawn know this
April one seasonal joy
Spring thro' winter endowing bliss
So make a wish when rainbow's ploy
Treasure hunts the pot of gold
Discover end of annus come
Summer sun, autumn leaves, winter frosty cold
So cast a spell, 'Dismal rain be joysome'
Secret desires one can see, can feel
Nature's woven change of clime
Welcome every treadled reel
Golden web, silver lining, spun thro' time.

Christina C Harkness

SPRINGTIME

Sunshine brings us warmth and light, when flowers blossom
                                        with delight.
Children play with squeals of joy, every girl and every boy.
Cheerful laughter all around, happy, pleasant, joyful sounds.
Springtime brings us sights and sounds of God's creation all around.
Bluebells, lilacs, daisies, grass, climbing, growing by the mass.
Through the earth they show their heads, some in fields, some
                                        flower beds.
Nature comes it's all for free, it's there for you and there for me.
Colours cheerful, bright and gay, pink and yellow, lilac, grey.
Easter brings us chocolate yummies, eggs and rabbits in our tummies.
Blackbird whistling in the trees, cuckoo singing songs to please.
Jumpers out and dresses on, hello springtime, winter's gone.
Lambs are jumping in the fields, farmers sowing crops to yield.
God gave us this time of peace, as Jesus died for hate to case.
He died for you and me that day and in a tomb they saw him laid.
His mother Mary saw him cry, he hung there torn and crucified.
His death, it wasn't all in vain, nor were his tears of fear and pain.
His father up in Heaven above, sent down His son with peace
                                        and love.
We celebrate His birth with cheer, why not His death, young
                                        children dear?
Please don't be sad, be full of joy, all little girls and little boys.
In death we celebrate a start, a new beginning, a loving heart.
If Jesus hadn't died that day, and come back happy, smiling, gay,
We wouldn't have our Easter bunnies and lots of chocolate in
                                        our tummies.

W A Evans

THE OLD MAN

He sat by the fire, silent and still,
And where he sat the air was quite chill,
His old-time clothes were threadbare and worn,
Some would say he was sad and forlorn,
Alone and lonely in the tavern,
Though his presence made many heads turn
And some folk paused in their stride to stare.

A young man walked slowly toward him,
The eerie figure was grey and grim,
And put down a pint of foaming ale,
'Drink this,' he said, 'you look a bit pale.
Pale as a ghost, if such things there be.'
The old man stood tall for all to see,
'Aye, so there be,' he cried - and vanished!

Ralph Smith

A CHILD'S WORLD

The world is full of magic,
You'll find it everywhere,
From the Christmas fairy lights
To a 'talking' teddy bear!
In fairgrounds, on steam trains,
To donkeys on a beach,
In flying kites on windy days,
Watching stars - far out of reach.
In seeing shadows on a wall,
Painting pictures in a book,
Playing football - your first goal,
Gathering frogspawn from a brook.
Dressing up in high-heeled shoes,
Wearing fancy dress.
In loving cuddles from your mum,
Whenever there's distress!
Childhood passes all too soon,
Those magic days are gone,
Then you have children of your own,
And that magic is passed on!

E M Eagle

UNICORN

In the moon glow, bright and white,
On the midnight's deep,
In the beams of dreaming light,
Over the city asleep,
On the clouds' white glaze,
Past the stars, on night's dark ways,
Something is softly stamping its feet.

Is it only the far thunder's beat?
Is it only a drifting, bright cloud
On the edge of the rise of the storm?
Or is it a prancing and proud,
Moon-born unicorn?

Its voice is the far ocean's swell,
It rides on the moon's silent beams;
Its horn is a white, spiralled shell,
Its path is the pathway of dreams.

On the edge of the rise of the storm,
Over the city asleep,
Is it a drift of bright cloud?
Or is it a prancing and proud,
Moon-born unicorn,
Softly, softly stamping its feet?

Mark Scrivener

MUDDY BUBBLES

Muddy shoes, muddy shoes,
Stamp! Stomp! Squelch!
Chase away the blues.

Splashing through the puddles,
Splish! Splash! Splosh!
Chase away the blues.

Home again, home again,
Hop! Run! Skip!
Chase away the blues.

Bubbly bath, bubbly bath,
Rub! Scrub! Glug!
Wash away the blues.

D Cheneler

HARRY WHO?

A colossal squid near the South Pole
Could not care less for storm or squall.
Whatever swam near, it took -
Because it could sling its hook . . .
It's the squiddiest squid of them all.

How can you communicate with it
Before those hooks tear you bit from bit?
'Squiddy, I come as a friend -
Not to meet a grisly end . . .'
I guess I'll let someone else risk it.

But – who? Perhaps someone called Harry
Will know just what to say or carry.
'Squiddy, you're under my spell.
You and I must get on well.
Undersea, we'll cope colossally . . .

You've eyes as big as a dinner plate,
No wonder your lunch is never late.
With your tentacles trailing
And our friendship unfailing -
Pals will be stunned to meet my new mate!'

Chris Creedon

DECKCHAIR

While away the hours and
Eat clotted cream for tea,
Read a book and take a nap
In a deckchair by the sea.

Sun and sea and sand,
Blue sky and clouds for free,
Cliffs so white they shine upon
A deckchair by the sea.

A pier, a fair, a circus,
And a candyfloss for me,
A parasol so colourful,
Over a deckchair by the sea.

Sand pie, castle and flag,
Do flutter and tide does flee,
And then it rushes up again
To my deckchair by the sea.

Oh I love the seaside,
It fills my heart with glee,
I could sit right here forever,
In my deckchair by the sea.

Wynn Stone

DEEP, DARK WOOD

In a deep, dark wood where nobody goes,
Live creatures strange, so it is told,
People who enter this mysterious place,
Have never returned to tell their tale.

All except one! Old Jeremiah,
Who told me his tale of this horrible place.

Deep down in the wood there is a lake,
Where there lives a serpent coloured bright red,
He lives off the blood of any man,
Who is foolish enough to cross his path.

Then there's Ragh, a bird with six heads,
Its colour is purple to match its rage.
Don't mess with this creature with eyes, back and front,
It will gobble you up with one gulp.

In the trees there live the flying monkeys,
Their colour is green and they are always hungry.
The noise they make will make you shudder,
As they try to eat one another.

There's a pride of lions with colours of every hue,
But the king of them all is Azure blue,
He's a mean old cat so watch your back,
From behind he will attack.

There are laughing frogs and singing bats,
Yellow spiders and insects that snatch,
But old Jeremiah told me one thing,
Of the creature that saved him from this awful scene.

A beautiful creature, its colour pure white,
With a horn on its head containing the elixir of life.
The unicorn was swift and brought him to safety,
And for this old Jeremiah was eternally grateful.

Jane Margaret Isaac

A TALE OF FROGS

Two frogs fell into a milk can one day
One was filled with terror
The other dismay:
'We're done for, we're done for,'
Frog No1 wailed
And very soon died
As his flabby courage failed.
No2 paid no heed to No1 -
He wouldn't succumb to fright:
'There must be a way –
There must be a way,'
He swam and he swam
From the bottom to the top
Then from the top to the bottom of the can.
Though his heart began to flutter
He put up a strong fight
And lo, his movements churned
The milk into butter
That put an end to his plight
He hopped out to safety
And grinned with wide-mouthed suavity.

Mary Frances Mooney

SPIDER-MAN'S SUPER SECRET!

Now I'm in love what should I do,
Admit I'm Spider-Man?
Say I'm the guy in red and blue
And hope that she's a fan?
Or send boxed flowers wrapped in web,
No strings attached at all?
Or boast that I'm a great celeb
With wisecracks that enthral?
Although it's cool to fly about,
My mask keeps me at bay . . .
And though my heart's so full of doubt,
I hope my feelings stay!
I see her smile, the world stands still . . .
She speaks and I go numb . . .
As if she stole my mind, my will
And I'm under her thumb!
I've got the strength of twenty men
Yet love makes me go weak!
Its power grows beyond my ken!
What makes her so unique?
To me, she is the only girl . . .
No other means so much!
I'm in her web! My heart's awhirl!
Love's so darned hard to budge!
To all the world I'm quite a catch -
All brave in red and blue . . .
Though Spider-Man is hard to match,
Should I say, *'I love you!'*?
If so, when is the moment right?
There's no escape from crime!
Love hurts just like a spider's bite!
Time after time after time . . .

Denis Martindale

ONE-EYED JACK

Jack is just a worn-out bear,
To you, a symbol of love and care,
He's got one eye and lost his hair,
You and Jack, a special pair.
Your upturned nose, his 'teddy' face,
He always travels in your case.
By your bed, his special place,
There's magic between you and Jack.
You smile at him and get one back,
Whisper him secrets, he will hear,
Into your heart he can peer,
Knowing every childhood fear.
He cries too if you shed a tear,
Jack the teddy is very dear,
A special friend, he's always near.

Sheila Walters

KIDNAPPED

Mother said if I count sheep, then I will surely fall asleep,
Yet here I am, make no mistake, midnight gone and still awake,

When suddenly before my eyes, completely taken by surprise,
A dragon swooped and kidnapped me, and flew me over land and sea,

Till all I knew was out of sight, vanishing into the night
To where I'd never been before, suspended from a giant claw,

Unto a place of alchemy, a place of myth and mystery,
A misty orange, eerie sight, where me and dragon would alight,

Elves and goblins to and fro, ghost-like creatures come and go,
Faces peer from every tree, ghouls and gremlins frighten me,

Witches fly through smelly fog, cackling from a bubbling bog,
I try to run, but cannot flee, for something grim is grasping me,

I turn and see a fleshless hand, restricting me to where I stand,
The ground around throws back its dead and fills me with a
powerful dread,

Limbs start shaking to extreme, stolen is my power to scream,
Howling comes a hooded head, 'Morning, come on get out of bed.'

Mom!

Brian Margetts

THOMAS THUMB

Thomas Thumb, what *have* you done to be abandoned so?
Baby Finger is as far away as she can be
And Finger Ring won't do a thing to keep you company,
Middle Finger will not linger, she stretches straight and tall,
Whilst Finger pointer will not loiter though closest of them all.
Thomas Thumb, what *have* you done to be abandoned so?

E Marcia Higgins

MY SPECIAL LITTLE BOY
(This poem is dedicated to my son, Ashley, with all my love)

I said I'd write a poem for you
And this is what I'm going to do.
I want you to know I love you so,
And always will, wherever you may go.

I have to mention your teddy bear,
Who from your first Christmas has always been there.
You always take him to your bed,
And I know that he will always remain your best friend.

You love the sand dunes and playing by the sea,
You also love picking the conkers as they fall from the tree.
You like playing football and flying your kite,
You also like going for a ride on your brand new bike.

You asked me to mention Zippy too,
And how could I forget your beloved Pikachu.
Your two older brothers often play with you
And love you dearly, as I do too.

When you grow up, as we all do,
I'd like you to keep this poem I've written for you.
And remember just how much you mean to me,
As you're my special little boy and you always will be.

Carole-Anne Boorman

SID MEETS A STAR

Sidney moved away with Dad and Mum.
He had asked, 'Can Charlie's grandad come?
I would miss him, gazing at the stars;
I feel sure he knows the way to Mars.'
'That astronomer shall stay behind,'
Sidney's pa announced, 'but never mind,
We are moving somewhere much more smart -
Stars!' he chortled, but it broke Sid's heart,
For would next-door Ned now stand forlorn
On that patch of moonshine on the lawn,
Excluding poor Sidney from the fun?
To be punished so, what had he done?
Then, 'I want to fly,' our Sidney spoke,
As he was quite an ambitious bloke.
'I want to adventure evermore,
Near to the stars the astronomer saw.
I would touch Jupiter, Venus too,
T'would be a wonderful thing to do!'
Sidney's dad said, 'Son, we all have dreams,
When we're little, cherish hairbrained schemes.
Forget those stars, climb in the loft
And find us a duster, clean and soft.
There's lots to do in a move like this.
We all have friends we are going to miss.'
Sadly, the boy to the new loft stepped,
Into darkness, a stranger, he crept,
But a star shone through where Sidney hid.
'Good luck!' it flashed, 'keep on flying, Sid.'

Ruth Daviat

AUTUMN POEM

When September comes,
The leaves will turn
To orange and yellow and brown.
When the days get short
And the cool winds blow,
They will fall upon the ground.

When October comes,
The days get cool
And we need our coats to play.
We watch the weather
Get foggy and wet
And the blue sky turns to grey.

When November comes,
The weather is cold
And sometimes it is snowing.
When we play outside
And run around,
Our faces are happy and glowing.

Jane Audrey Edwards

BILLY'S SURPRISE

T'was Christmas Eve, and all was still,
When Billy heard tapping on his window sill,
He wandered over and opened the blind,
You'll never guess who he did find!

Father Christmas all dressed in red,
'I'm sorry Billy to get you out of bed,
But your chimney's blocked and your doors are locked,
I have lots of toys, for good girls and boys.'

So Billy opened the window wide and let Santa climb inside,
His bright red suit was covered in snow,
And his rosy-red cheeks sure did glow.
'It's cold outside, I've been there a while,'
Said Santa with a great big smile.

'I hear you've been good to your mum and dad,
I don't give toys if children are bad,
I have toys and games for you to play,
But you've not to open till Christmas Day.'

Billy stared, all tongue-tied, mouth and eyes open wide,
Santa Claus all red and white,
In my bedroom on Christmas night!
Billy helped Santa with his sack, his beard pure white, his
                                        boots jet black,
'Goodnight Billy, it's time to go, Rudolph gets chilly left in the snow.'
So out he climbed and said goodbye,
But not before having his milk and mince-pie!

Mandy Keay

CLOUD (NO 1)

Black patches of spots
Here and there in the sky
Like a flock of blackbirds
Here and there they always fly.

At times when full of rain
Thou drops down as showers
And with the soothing drops
Then quench the thirsty flowers.

Sometimes thou art fierce
Doing horrible devastations,
And again at times, it's thou
So kind to maintain the creation.

I pray to thee, oh dear cloud,
Be good enough to come down
On this earth at the burial ground
And shed thy tears on the shrouds.

A K Paul

HARRY'S NOT HOUDINI

Into, yes, his playpen,
Harry is calmly put,
Then he plans escape, you know,
After Mother's put her
Foot outside the door,
Caught out by the phone.
Goes around the playpen,
Tired, so ends up prone.
Woken for his dinner,
Today Harry has a treat,
Apple sauce, it says on tin,
After cauliflower cheese,
It's sweet.

M D Bedford

THE MOUSE

Someone stole the moon - I saw no one pass by,
The blackened shadows loom - across the darkened sky.
Not even one small star - looking back at me,
Glistening from afar - grateful I must be . . .
For my little home - free from damp and cold,
And the garden gnome - standing large and bold
Just outside my door - hiding me from harm,
Good food in my store - life's at present calm,
In my little house - cosy, warm and free,
Just right for a mouse - and his family.

Pearl M Burdock

FUNNY OLD LAND

I think I dreamed of something weird or did I?
I remember seeing a bright yellow sky,
With purple clouds and a crimson sun,
And strange little creatures having fun.

These creatures had two purple heads,
Orange arms and lime green legs.
They looked at me and waved a hand,
It seemed a friendly sort of land.

Flying high in the yellow sky above
Was what looked like a monkey crossed with a dove.
Crying aloud it had swooped down on me,
Maybe everything wasn't so friendly.

Then I was taken by the arm,
By the two-headed creatures that meant no harm.
They hid me until the danger had gone,
Then we had tea, I think it was jelly and a scone.

Did I imagine all of these things?
Was it real or was it one of my dreams?
I guess I will never really know,
But all the same, it was fun to go.

Lynn Mottram

FAIRY

Light and airy,
Charming and chary,
Are the ingredients to make a fairy,
Sleight of hand,
Wondrous wand,
I have to beg your pardon,
Are there fairies at the bottom of your garden?
Would you tell,
As they cast their spell
At the bottom of your bed each night,
Diaphanous delight,
They dazzle your very sight,
With their steps so quicksilver and light,
They live beneath toadstools,
Their wings shimmer like glorious jewels,
But they can be as stubborn as mules,
Humans they think of as fools.
So if you catch sight
Of a fairy in mid-flight,
For she will see you're all right,
But remember, they only come out at night.

Alan Pow

A BEDTIME PRAYER

When I lay me down to sleep in His tender arms
As His comfort radiates He keeps me from alarms
Safe in His surroundings as on His blessed breast
He is my rock and refuge, He gives me total rest
He listens when I talk to Him in my childish way
Letting me describe those plans that happened during the day
His advice I cling to, He takes me by the hand
Preparing me for my night's rest then into dream land
I have prayed and asked forgiveness for all those wrongs I did
He smiles and absolves and comforts me, even those childish fibs
Listening as I ramble on, He knows and understands
I hear and know He prays for me as my night rest He plans.

R D Hiscoke

THE OSTRICH

Have you ever seen an ostrich?
He's a very funny bird,
He has such stringy, beanpole legs
And also, so I've heard,
If anybody frightens him
(At least, so it is said)
He digs a hole right in the dirt
And in it puts his head!

It can't be very comfortable
To stand with neck stretched out!
To try to balance in the dark,
Not move one's head about!
I think he would do better
If he used his big, flat feet
To run as fast as he could go
To the policeman on his beat!

Peggy Hemmings

MIRVIN AND MILDRED

Mirvin and Mildred
Were mice
And they lived in the house
Of Beryl and Bryce

A hole by the oven
Was home to them both
Quite convenient for crumbs
From a freshly-baked loaf

And just a short trip
Across to the larder
Then the fridge was only
A little bit farther

Mirvin was fearless
And hunted at night
While Mildred kept watch
'Til it was light

Due to the fact that
The house had a cat
Mirvin and Mildred
Were wise

As the kitchen was wide
And so small was their stride
They had to be quick
To avoid cat's surprise

Mildred would sew
All the buttons and bows
On cushions and pillows
And all of their clothes

While Mirvin would sit
In a chair made of sticks
Gently rocking and smoking
His pipe

A mouse world all snuggly
And cosy and nice
With cheese bits for supper
And a pudding of rice

And upstairs above them
Oblivious to this
Lay yawning and snoring
Beryl and Bryce.

A R White

NURSERY NONSENSE

There's a terrible muddle in Nursery Rhyme Land
They're having the most awful time,
You see just for a joke they all ran amok
And now they can't find their own rhyme.

Take Little Boy Blue, now what can he do?
There should be a cow in the corn
But he keeps finding sheep and meeting Bo Peep
And she's dragging a bull by one horn.

And as for the King, he can't dance and sing,
For he can't find his fiddlers. Why?
Well, they sat in the corner with Little Jack Horner
And they're covered completely with pie.

Humpty Dumpty's jumped over the moon
And he's hovering somewhere in space,
And Jack's hurt his crown, by tumbling down
From the wall when he took Humpty's place.

And guess who's moved into the gingerbread house?
Why, the lady who lived in the shoe,
But she's eaten the roof and to tell you the truth,
The walls will soon get eaten too.

Tom, Tom the piper's son, ran away with the dish and the spoon
And the pig's on the tuffet with Little Miss Muffet,
And the spider?
There isn't much room.

Ding Dong Bell, the cat's not in the well,
Contrary Mary's swimming for her life,
And Tweedle Dum and Dee are sitting down to tea,
That should belong to Jack Sprat and his wife.

So the King has sent for the Duke of York
And his ten thousand men,
To round them up and take them back to their nursery rhymes again.
And there they'll stay for evermore,
They'll stay until the end of time.
And each girl and boy will hear with joy
Their favourite nursery rhyme.

J Fedorski

FAMOUS DREAMS

I always wonder what it would be like, to be a famous star,
To be on the telly, and ride in a chauffeur-driven car.
Maybe a pop star, or an actor in a soap?
Or a famous writer, comedian or a pope!
Everyone would know my face, I'd be in all the news
And I'd go on lots of chat shows and people would listen to my views.
I'd have a personal cook, to make my favourite dish
And enough money to buy anything that I wish.
I'd buy myself an island, somewhere sunny and hot,
A place nice and private, where trespassers would be shot!
My clothes would be made out of fifty-pound notes,
And a gold name tag painted on all my twenty boats.
I'd do so good for others, the Queen would make me a knight
And I'd buy myself another brain to make me really bright.
Days would be spent lazing in the sun,
Swimming, dancing or shopping, spending money on everyone.
All the other famous people would think I was great,
They'd all fight to see who would be my best mate.
Who knows, one day my wishes may come true
And you'll see me on the telly, staring back at you.

Nicky Pitchers

THE FROG

The life of a frog is really no joke,
His singing voice is a low-pitched croak.
Long, strong back legs will let him leap
And also swim in the pond so deep.
He comes from an egg in the middle of spawn
Which hatches out in the warmth after dawn.
Now has a large tail and a big black head
And quickly grows when he's properly fed.
Back legs first, then front legs too,
The tail goes then with nought to do.
Then soon from the water and out from the bog,
There comes a lovely and perfect little frog.

David Hammond

A WITCH AND HER CAT

A witch and her cat
Dusted off her old broom
'Tonight,' said the witch,
'We fly off to the moon.'

So they waited until
All the stars had come out
'To the moon and beyond,'
Cried the witch with a shout.

They flew and they flew
For a year and a day
'Goodness me,' said the witch,
'It is such a long way.'

But at last they arrived
And they both tumbled down
'Goodness me,' said the witch
And she started to frown.

For all of the flowers
And bushes and trees
Were made of the most
Delicious cheese.

The cat used his claw
And he cut off a slice
'You should try some,' he said,
'It is ever so nice.'

There they sat on the moon
Eating Cheddar and Brie
The cat whistled a tune
As the witch ate her tea.

And before very long
Both their tummies were fat
While the cat sang a song
The witch took off her hat.

'Let us stay here,' she said,
'Cos there's plenty to eat.'
'I agree,' said the cat,
'Cheese is nicer than meat.'

So they stayed, and I think
They are still there today
And they're still eating cheese
Along some milky way.

The cat uses his claw
The witch has a spoon
And between them so far
They've eaten half of the moon.

So tonight if you wait
'Til it's dark in the sky
And you see only half a moon
Now you know why!

H Phillips

ALL SIXES AND SEVENS

I'm awfully like David Beckham,
I can bend the ball and make it curl,
And the boys say I'm magic at tackling,
Not bad for a six-year-old girl!

I'm terribly bad on Mum's mobile,
I phoned someone once in Madrid,
Then I put in a call to Australia
To tell Aunty Flo what I did!

But I'm awfully good at computers,
When Daddy gets into a mess,
If he promises me a McDonald's,
I tell him which button to press.

I'm terribly good at my reading,
When Gran buys me Winnie the Pooh,
I swap it for Harry Potter
In W H Smith - wouldn't you?

Though I sometimes make Daddy quite angry,
And I make Mummy holler and shriek,
I am awfully grown-up already,
And I'm going to be *seven* next week!

Peter Davies

TOBY'S CHOCOLATE BISCUIT

If Nanna had two and Grandad three,
Mum had one with her cup of tea.
Lulu and Sam had two each, cos I see 'em.
Molly ate two and gave one to our Liam.
If the two that I had were the mid of the pack,
We were halfway done when Dad came back.
He was dipping and munching, I made it four,
Then the neighbours turned up at our front door.
On went the kettle, out came the tin,
Quite a few more later, and one in the bin.
I've added, divided and come to this sum,
There's a biscuit in the barrel . . . just the one.

And when no one's looking,
It's mine,
All mine!

Suzie Burton

FAIRY CHILD

On dragonfly wings
A fairy fair
Like cobweb spun
Her fairy hair

Two mulberry leaves
Stuck with cuckoo spit
Her dress entire
With sunlight lit

Antenna curled and ready
Like a butterfly
That tremble when hearing
You, a young child, cry.

I R Finch

IT CAME FROM THE SEA

It was just a crofter's cottage near the sea, but Kate had made it habitable and spent most of the summer there. As a writer, she took her inspiration from the sea.

Kate pulled her car onto the sandy beach, picked up her things and left them in the cottage. She sat on the sand listening to the sound of the waves from the sea. She began to feel sleepy and went into the cottage, where she fell into a deep sleep.

During the time she slept, the weather changed; a storm blew up, the wind howled, the rain fell, it became bitter cold, snowflakes fell, the sea roared, the waves rose higher and higher. Kate slept on.

Something appeared in the cottage, like a man with a face like a fish, gills on the side of his face, his feet and hands were like giant fins. He called to Kate in a stereotype voice and trance-like she followed. Kate found herself at the bottom of the sea. She saw a castle covered in diamonds, the floor was covered in jewels of all colours. She looked up and looking back at her were others like the creature.

Kate woke up, everything looked the same. The sun still shone through the window. She walked to the door to see large fin-like prints going back to the sea. Was it a dream? If so, what were the fin-like shapes in the sand?

Jean Bailey

SEVEN STAGES OF WOMAN

Although so many alike,
Still the female child is unique.
Born like a flower,
Fresh in bud,
Blown in the breeze of life,
Innocent and unaware of worldly sins.
Reaching up and growing aware,
Finding life's puzzle a joke,
In her gigglish schoolday ways.
At the height of success,
Fate is spread before her
In paths of sophisticated life.
Challenge and competition for employment,
Security favoured.
She is sought after by the hands of lovers,
Spasmodic romances slip away.
Under her white veil,
Caught like a spider
In a web of chores.
She bears the child,
Mother Nature ties her instinctively to this life form
Until, slipping from the grasp of aged hands,
Her child becomes a mother.
In a never-ending cycle,
This one flower has withered,
But love means:-
The family tree is alive and mighty.

Julie Spackman

DAVID'S FIRST DAY

I'm a little bit scared
And nervous
'Cause I'm starting school today
I've got a new uniform
Tie and black shoes
And a bag
With my plimsolls to play
We had to get up
Really early
Dropped Emily off
At playschool
Mummy said, 'You're my big boy
Don't you know
Because only big boys
Go to school'
Daddy is standing there
By the school gate
Gives me a big hug
And says
'You're my little man
And don't you look smart'
As we walk into school
Through the gate.

Jeanette Gaffney

THE BUTTON FAMILY ADVENTURES

The Button family live on a pink cardigan,
In six-year-old Molly Millington's drawer,
There's Ma and Pa, Betty and Bert,
And baby Boo, Bonnie and Benny the twins.
Once baby Boo was trapped inside a giant soap bubble
In the washing machine,
Until she shot like a catapult on spin cycle to freedom.
Pop!

Another time in the wash, Benny sneezed
And flew straight past a Shetland woolly jumper,
Landing inside a navy blue sock
Belonging to Molly's dad.
He wasn't found until a fortnight later,
When he came into close contact with a human's toe,
For a whole day.
Pong!

Next day he had to endure the painful operation,
Known as sewing,
Ouch!
On the day of the latest adventure,
Molly joined her friend Rosie on her garden swing,
As high into the air they went,
Bonnie came loose and whizzed through the air,
Landing in a jungle of tall grass.

Then Rosie's foot caught her like tiddlywinks
And she found herself at the paws of Clarence the cat.
Miaow!
Due to an unexpected, torrential rainstorm,
She splashed into a rivulet of water near a drain,
Plop!

The perilous journey was brought to an end
As Molly retrieved Bonnie on her way home.

'Another button's fallen off again, Mum,' she said.
If only she knew of the family's adventures.

Ann G Wallace

HARRY WHO?

Locked in my bedroom
away from the world,
my book pours out magic,
my mind is uncurled,
with broomsticks I fly
and dart through the sky,
over the tree tops
my mates and I fly.

This net is spun
with words I enjoy,
the hero, like me,
is only a boy,
each day an adventure,
a journey to school,
teachers are wizards,
it really is cool.

So entranced
I turn the page,
I see the postman,
an owl in a cage.
I hear the voice
that calls me for tea,
'Oh Mum! Not now,
please leave me be!'

Sally Flood

DRAGONS

There was a dragon long ago
That fought St George as well you know.
Dragons tall and dragons small
Some with feet, some with no feet at all
Jagged spikes and scales that glisten
Blazing eyes in rainbows prism
Some are green and some are red
Some are yellow with a purple head
Some have claws that rip and tear
And a serpent's tongue that snaps from its lair
Some are vicious and some are nice
Some eat people but are scared of mice
Some breathe fire that flare and flash
And some will settle for sausage and mash
A Chinese dragon is lucky and true
A Japanese dragon guards the gates of jade blue
The golden dragon weighs the truth
The Welsh dragon is brave, proud and aloof
The dragon breathes fire and molten breath
And bodes its enemies a fiery death
Sometimes a dragon will change its features
And be more magical than all Earth's creatures
I have travelled high and travelled low
And still can't discover where dragons go
I've searched mountains and forests and lakes far and wide
But before I get there the dragons hide
Of all the things that are elusive
The dragon by far is the most exclusive
And one thing I want before I die
Is to see a dragon with my own eye.

Hawkins

Circus Time

Mum says we're going to the circus,
It sounds really cool.
I've heard there will be some sea lions,
Balancing balls in a paddling pool.

Mum says we're going to the circus,
It sounds really great.
I've heard there will be a magician,
Who pulls thing out from a magic crate.

Mum says we're going to the circus,
It sounds like *loads* of fun,
I've heard there will be acrobats,
Who perform daring stunts.

Mum says we're going to the circus,
It sounds really good,
I've heard there will be clowns,
Who drive a car made out of wood.

Mum *did* say we were going to the circus,
But her car has broken down.
It sounded really exciting,
But now I'm wearing a frown.

Mrinalini Dey (12)

BUMBLY BEE

Bumbly Bee flew high in a tree
And stung poor Olly the owl,
Who fell on a hump, that started to bump,
He'd landed Nelly the cow.
Now Nelly took fright and
Ran through the night,
Then finally stopped by a lock,
But fell in a groove that started to move
The jaws of Freddy the croc.
Freddy ate Nelly, so slept by a pool
And dreamt of his meal in the dark,
But drifted to sea and was finally
Swallowed by Sammy the shark,
But Sammy was heavy and swam too far
And landed himself in a gale,
Then high on a wave, he entered a cave,
Was the mouth of Willy the whale.

John Wayre

IS IT A MONSTER?

There is something under my bed,
Two big arms and one enormous head.

Is it a monster? I do not know,
Underneath I am scared to go.

Two big eyes, or are there more?
Great long legs I can see for sure.

Is it a monster? I do not know,
Underneath I am scared to go.

Bending down, I can see a nose
And there's a mouth, I hope it's closed.

Is it a monster? I do not know,
Underneath I am scared to go.

It is very dark, I cannot see,
Is this thing looking at me?

Is it a monster? I do not know,
Underneath I am scared to go.

Should I get out and turn on the light?
I'm really not sure if this thing will bite.

Is it a monster? I do not know,
Underneath I am scared to go.

Feeling quite brave, I pull back the sheet,
Not quite sure what I will meet.

Is it a monster? I do not know,
Underneath I am going to go.

Slowly, slowly, feet on the ground,
Being so careful not to make a sound.

Down on my knees, look under the bed,
It's not a monster, it's my big ted.

So don't be scared to look under the bed.
There are no monsters, just toys instead.

Leanne Thompson

RUNNING TO SCHOOL

Blocked by danger all the way
By soldiers, bullets, guns
The terrifying obstacles
For daughters and for sons

Dodging gunshots aimed at them
These children run to school
From Israel's deadly strategy,
Their callous Nazi tool

Climbing over walls then crouching
Judging when to dash
Scrambling for safety
As the weapons roar and flash

Challenging the State
That would deny their right to learn
Palestinian children take
Their chances and their turn.

Kim Montia

APPLES AND STARS

Apple so golden, high on the bough
Will you not fall?
I cannot reach you -
I am so small.

Mama tells me you
Have a lesson to teach -
How what a child wants
Often lies beyond reach.

And if I wish for the prize
I must aspire
To grow like the apple tree
Higher and higher.

But when darkness steals daylight
I look at the star
Seeming near, stretch my hand out,
But the star is too far -

Then slumbering, wander
In dream of a land
Where apples and stars,
Gold and silver, fall into my hand.

Startled awake, I find in my palm
Neither silver nor gold -
No stars, nor apples to charm
Me - then vainly I clasp
At faraway apples
And stars beyond grasp.

Terry Smith

SPELLBOUND

'Joey are you sure we should be in here,
After all, it is the wizard's home.
Where is the wizard now, then Joey?'
'Oh, he flew off with Shangri-La Airlines,
To a wizards' convention in Winnipeg for two weeks.
I just want to know, when he casts a spell,
In which language he speaks.

Look, there's his book of spells and tales,
And his wand of glass.'
'Put it down Joey, you don't know its power,
You might turn us into blocks of ice
That take a thousand years to melt,
And when we return after all that time,
Father might fetch his belt,

Joey, I'm leaving now, I'm uneasy in this place.
It's spooky, eerie and it smells.'
'Toby, stay a bit longer, I won't touch anything,
Look when will we ever get another chance
To see a real live wizard's den.'
'Well all right Joey, but only another ten minutes then.'

'Look, here's the wizard's hat and cloak,
I'll try them on.'
'No, don't Joey.'
'Don't worry Toby, it'll be all right,
Look at me Toby, like a real wizard.'
'Joey, look at all these cups and plaques,
He must be a champion wizard Joey,
He has runner-up rosettes in stacks.'

'Toby, I'm going to try a spell,
What shall we turn into?'
'No Joey, it's time to go.
'Hocus pocus, Shim, Sham, Shaboo,
No more homework and no more school.'
Suddenly Joey is the Caped Crusader
And I am the Riddler playing the fool.

P J Littlefield

THE PRETENDERS

We used to make mud pies
'For dinner,' we would say
And Mum would say, 'A good idea,'
In a muddy mess we'd play.

We used to play at shop,
With toys, books, empty boxes and packets,
A miniature cash till with a bell
And cardboard money for our pockets.

Mum and Dad often trimmed our hair
So we entered the hairdressing trail
When Emily's golden locks took our fancy,
We hung them on the towel rail.

One rainy day we played at being Mums,
Our dolls bodies of papier-mâché were fated,
We sat them in a bowl of hot water,
Where the legs and bottoms disintegrated.

Our upturned desk became a boat
In the middle of a lake,
We swam across the carpet
And helped each other to be safe.

Kathleen McBurney

OLD MR RUTSHOCK

Old Mr Rutshock sat against the wall,
He was thinking back to when he was small.
When he was a toddler, he *was* a cheeky brat,
Always beating Granny with his little cricket bat.
At school, he played the fool and tormented all his teachers,
By filling up his school bag with cockroaches and leeches.
When he was a teenager, he started to smoke,
But soon gave up as it made him choke.
When he was a young man, he found an occupation
As a doctor and he put a stop to people's constipation.
Back in the present, Mr Rutshock sighed,
He'd had a good life.
He smiled and died.

Ellis Creez

A Fairy Rhyme

On hearing the glossy blackbird's song
The fairies will not be long
As they dance in their ring
One rests on a bell
To signal all is well
There are many tales to tell
As elf and fairy leap
Children fall asleep
Human and fairy are as one
In a garden
In the setting sun.

Paul Wilkins

THE CHARGE OF THE BEETLES' BRIGADE

A thousand of them at full pelt
Here, there and everywhere.
The sergeant's puffing out his cheeks
And muttering like a gun reports:
'Screwdrivers at the ready there.
You're like a band of butterflies in shorts.
I've never seen the like of it in weeks!'

One trailed his drums; five saucepans on a leash.
Another had a hunting horn,
A string of onions, a rotten peach.
None with more sense than he was born.

An ice cram vendor played his chimes
Upon a distant lonely hill.
The sergeant gave the sign to charge,
They all regrouped in nines and ran
Banners flying up and ready still,
A towelling nappy on the foremost man.
A fighting, spitting army on the large
And climbing up the window sill.

Diane Burrow

SPIDERS

There are spiders in my house
and they never make webs.
They have soft, squashy bodies
and great long, hairy legs.
They walk across the ceiling
with slow majestic gait.
Scuttle down the skirting board
just in case they're late.
They lurk in the corner
and seem to stand and stare.
Disappear! Where do they go?
Where is their secret lair?

Ivy Allpress

MY FRIEND THE SNAIL

Digging in the garden,
The grass was damp with showers,
Little head peeped out
Looked round about,
Sampled some sweet flowers.
I wanted to be friendly,
Tapped upon the door,
When fat snail saw me coming near,
Rushed in and closed the door.

I left Snail in the flower bed,
Went to have my tea,
When I came back
Snail was travelling fast,
House on back,
Never looked at me.

Seemed in such a hurry,
Perhaps I'll wait and see,
Then a big, black crow
Dropped like a stone,
Carried poor Snail high up to her nest
In the hawthorn tree.

I called out, 'Snail, I'm sorry
Your friend I wished to be.
I wanted to play in the garden
With you, but you closed
The snail house door on me.'

Frances Gibson

GOING TO THE ZOO

Jeremy Huw went to the zoo
On a bright summer's day.
On his red hat, sat his black cat,
Mewing the live-long day.

Draped on his back was a small sack
Holding some crisps to eat.
Little he knew, a tiny shrew
Crept in on noiseless feet.

Jeremy saw a monkey's paw
Reaching in stealthily,
Open the sack, soon jumping back,
Tiny shrew leaping free.

'Miaow,' mewed the cat (on the red hat)
'Shrews make a yummy snack.'
Off bounced the shrew, he almost flew -
Onto the tiger's shack.

'Grrr,' roared the beast, 'not a big feast,
Eating a shrew is weird.'
One mighty jump, onto its hump,
Just as the camel appeared.

Jeremy Huw said that the zoo
Was not the best place to go.
Even the cat (on the red hat)
Said a very loud, *'No.'*

Stephanie Stone

WHEN I RODE ON A WITCH'S BROOMSTICK

When I rode on a witch's broomstick,
At 1400mph in the air,
I swivelled around
Looking down at the ground
And held on tight to me hair.

When I rode on a witch's broomstick,
Flying out like a giant, wood' fork,
I didn't too mind
Cos you see I do find
It's more exciting than having to walk.

When I rode on a witch's broomstick,
And landed right next to my school,
I said, 'Can't I stay?
Witch, I've had a fun day
And I don't want to go there at all!'

But witchey replied with a frown on her face,
'Horrid child (cackle, cackle) school now!
Or I'll turn you to frog,
Ugly elephant or dog
Or big, mooey, mooey old cow.'

I didn't dare argue - oh not with a witch,
Made my way to the grey classroom door,
And boasted to friends
With their Jags and Mercedes Benz
About my trip in a broomstick 4.4.

Yes I rode on a witch's broomstick:
It's not something that most people do.
And if you look late at night;
See a 1400mph broom in the light
That'll be witch Flumsrelda Casoo.

Laura McClelland

MOJACCA

Down in Mojacca where the dweebol birds sing,
And the ferris goes plop and the flugal goes ping,
Where the grunge-wobbler flanges and the shadely-bobber grows,
There stood Nelly Toadgrin, with a sneevil on her nose!
The sneevil, Gorbellin Mahatandmacoat,
Green-bellied the wench and got stuck in her throat,
'Sneevil Crisis In Mojacca!' the local rag read,
'Nelly Toadgrin copped a gobful and wound up rather dead.'
Grewber McWerter had seen the affair,
But Grewber McWerter wasn't all there,
A man can't be trusted, who would usually be . . .
Dressed like a nun, halfway up a tree.
He pointed the finger at Spingly of Cray,
Who'd been seen with a sneevil the previous day,
Poor Grewber, it seemed, was out of his fish,
For Spingly of Cray was a casserole dish!
But the law is the law and they arrested the dish
And put Grewber McWerter back in his fish,
The dish was found guilty and sentenced to life,
The fish and McWerter are now man and wife.

Nicholas Godsell

ROBIN

Red-breasted friend of garden table
a legend born of myth and fable.
Little eye black and bright
songs sung deep into night.
Bringing cheer and total delight
to enter the thorns
Only he was able.

Andrew McIntyre

TO KELLIE

There is a magic garden
But it's not up in the sky,
It's right here, all around us,
Before our very eyes.

And in the gentle flowers
God has poured His own perfume,
And when we hear the songs of little birds,
We're hearing God's own tunes.

Yes, everywhere we look,
Up and down and left and right,
It should make us happy just to know
We're always, in God's sight.

Blanche Helena Hall

RAT SCHOOL

(From the musical, 'The Piper' by David Gasking)

One rat and then another rat
 That gives you two rats in all
Two rats and two together
 Makes it a bit more full
And when it comes to four rats and four?
 Why should we bother to count them at all?
Well the solution is easy to see
 More rats and more rats and more, more, more.

One rat and two rats, three rats and four
Soon you will have a whole lot more
These are the lessons rat kids must learn
Then there'll be rats wherever you turn

 We've been to Rat School we know the score
 All round the dustbins, under the floor
 No sweat, no trouble, no fuss
 Just leave it up to us

Fling out your rubbish, add to the pile
Throw out your junk and leave it a while
Multiplication, that's what we do best
No need to worry, we'll do the rest

 We've been to Rat School we know the score
 All round the dustbins, under the floor
 No sweat, no trouble, no fuss
 Just leave it up to us

David Gasking

THE MONKEY

From his lookout perch
in the tree so high
monkey drops coconuts
on surprised passers by.
Rubbing their head they
look up and gape
at the face staring down
of a grinning ape.

Monkey walks among
the tall jungle trees,
his arms swinging well
below his knees.
Some animals use stealth
as they quietly stalk,
but not the monkey
with his chattering talk.

Monkey knows where the
best banana grows
and attempts to peel
one with his toes.
The agility of a monkey
is very clear to see
his long arms help him
swing from tree to tree.

Moon Stone

FAIRIES

At the bottom of my garden there are fairies I know,
I've seen them oh, so many times
As they dance around the trees,
Gossamer wings shining in soft moonlight's glow.

There are fairies at the bottom of my garden,
They play and laugh and sing,
With voices like tinkling silver bells
And light as thistledown.

I curl up on my window seat
And hug my favourite teddy,
And watch the whirl of golden hair
And flower-coloured dresses.

When the moon has slipped below the hills
And dawn comes with silver glow,
The garden is suddenly empty,
And they are gone, I know.

One night when I feel very brave,
With faithful ted for company,
I'll venture out to the shadowy trees
And see if they will play with me.

Sheila Giles

GRUMPY GRANDAD

I love my grandad, but sometimes he's a grump.
He likes to watch the telly and have a sneaky trump!

One day I said to Grandad, 'Will you play with me?'
'I'll play with you later, when I've had my cup of tea.'

Oh my grumpy grandad, he's always drinking tea.
I think he likes his tea, better than playing with me.

Well, we'll see about that, cos I've got a plan.
Next time I'll make the tea, for him and my nan.

'Do you want another cuppa?' I said to the old grump.
He said, 'That's a good idea,' as he did a sneaky trump.

Right, I'll make a start; I'll make his cup of tea!
And after he has drunk it, he'll wish he'd played with me.

So I got Grandad's mug and everything I'd need,
Chilli, garlic, toothpaste and some aniseed.

I stirred all the mixture and poured it in his mug.
Grandad drank it all, with a *glug, glug, glug!*

I waited for a minute, for the fun to start.
Then that was it, off the grump did dart.

He ran around the lounge, dancing all about.
He was pointing at his mouth, but he couldn't even shout.

Out of his mouth came a big orange flame!
It shot out his false teeth, with such an accurate aim.

Cos his teeth landed on the fire and they went up in smoke!
And I thought, *what have I done? I think he's going to croak.*

Steam came from his head and whistled down his nose
And there were even flames coming from his toes.

When it all calmed down, Grandad said to me,
'What on earth did you put in my cup of tea?'

I said, 'Nothing much, it was my new recipe.
I made it for you special, cos you wouldn't play with me!'

Karon Crocombe

ONCE IN A HUNDRED YEARS

The twins, little Alan and Jenny, were in bed while Mum read
from a book,
They wanted to hear all the nursery rhymes and Mum read - for
as long as it took
Eventually both fell asleep and Mum put the book down on the floor,
She tiptoed out of their bedroom and quietly closed the door.

Tonight was a magical evening that happened once in a hundred years
A night that was all celebration with no sadness or unhappy tears.
Slowly a little light glowed, surrounding the book on the floor,
Then all the characters came out of the book, one by one and then
by the score.

Miss Muffet directed her spider to help Insey spin webs that
would shine,
They would light up the whole celebration, while they watched
and they danced and they dined.
Mary was not so contrary as she placed flowers and bells all around,
The decorations were stunning, and the twins never heard a sound.

Humpty, Miss Muffet and little Bo Peep sat on a wall of cork,
They watched the parade of all his men being led by the Duke of York.
The music began with the fiddlers three and Boy Blue joined in
with his horn,
Tommy Tucker began to sing with the band and a musical night
was born.

The Queen of Hearts supplied all the tarts and the baker's man
the cakes,
Jack Horner prepared all the fruit you could eat and the Spratts
ate all they could take.
Everyone had such a wonderful time but soon it would all have to end,
As dawn approached they all had to go back, and Mary her lamb
to tend.

All signs of the night were swiftly removed, and the glow round
the book went away,
The twins began stirring from a dreamless sleep, at the start of a
brand new day.
It's been said that every hundred years that go by, a magical
night appears,
But no one has ever witnessed this night, perhaps it *is* true, my dears.

M McDonald

THE DRAGON

There's a dragon in my wardrobe,
I've seen him there at night.
The first time that I noticed him,
He gave me quite a fright.

I think he's very tidy,
For I've never round a mess.
But I find little tell-tale signs,
Upon my floor, no less.

Shiny scales of emerald green,
Lay by the wardrobe door.
Where he drags his tail inside,
I wonder if it's sore?

Sometimes when I'm laid in bed,
I smell his 'dragon smoke'.
If he scorches all my clothes,
That wouldn't be a joke.

He's a very cultured dragon,
When he thinks that I can't hear,
If I listen very carefully,
I hear him quoting Shakespeare.

I'm not a bit afraid of him,
He's more afraid of me.
I wonder, would it break the ice
If I invited him to tea?

I don't think that he would come,
Because he's very shy.
I'd love for him to be my friend,
I really ought to try.

Marisa Greenaway

Dragon Lord!

Majestically he stands - towering over his master,
dwarfing him with his mammoth proportions.
As his outspread wings in purple haze - aglow,
awaiting instruction - or to avoid disaster,
so thereby bequeath his lord a show.

It's from within his mist-filled, enormous cavern,
a quagmire of hazardous defences quiver,
enshrouding his existence from outer world.
Allowing rest and regeneration,
till once again he ventures to come forth.

A single beam of light penetrates the dark,
from the gaping orifice up high - stark.
The entrance of his personal domain,
where he shelters for his periodical refrain.

Stalagmite and stalactites abound,
decorating his lair form ceiling to ground.
While insignificant, slithery creatures unseen,
are so unpretentiously strewed,
flying and scurrying at every sound.

Disenfranchised from those of his own kind,
still he struggles and serves a mystic mind.
Until some day control is lost,
releasing him finally with horrendous cost,
becoming his own master and boss.

Gary J Finlay

SEA DREAMS

As I walk upon the seashore with soft sand beneath my feet,
I hear the waves moving to their own special beat,
Of crashing on the rocks that stand majestically high,
Then receding back to the sea with a whispering sigh.

If I were able to part the waves then take a look below
I would see an assortment of things, lying there on show.
The pretty coloured fishes, darting hither thither,
The great white shark, that makes me want to shiver.
Little baby sea horses that look so very sweet
And all the tiny creatures that they enjoy to eat.
The sea is such a fortress with many treasures still untold,
And it's been there forever, or at least I'm told.

So all walk upon the seashore,
Build your castles in the sand,
And let us hope it stays intact
From man's destructive hand.

Kim Shea

MAGICAL WALK
(For Hannah with love)

Floating through a canopy of trees
Sunday evening in a jaunty breeze
Bluebells spreading veil of fragrant hue
I roam Peter Pan trail sweet and new.

Fairies I see twirling so lightly
Pan pipes' sweet notes beckon 'come' brightly
Father Time intrudes, I'm lost, bereft,
Twilight creeps, stealing what day is left.

Shadows lengthen, frail carpet of lace
Western sun slips to a distant haze
Rustling wildlife scurry and scatter
Frisson of fear makes my heart flutter.

Stumbling I flee, trees tapping my face
Purple sky casts a veil over that place
Magic flown, no longer a bower
What dark secret does that wood cover?

Kathleen Potter

SNAIL

You carry your shell upon your back.
Snail! Tell me, is it heavy?
Your antennae protrude forward.
Snail! Tell me, can you see me?
You slither along leaving a silver slime.
Snail! Tell me, what's it mean?
You straddle the brown earth moving slowly.
Snail! Tell me why you do so.
You climb the cabbage leaves in the garden.
Snail! Tell me, do you eat them?
You come upon my doorstep sometimes.
Snail! Tell me, are you visiting?
Your silver marks remain long after.
Snail! Tell me why you leave them.
You've come to see me at my homestead.
Snail! Tell me, are you homesick?
Snail! Tell me if that is so.

Joan E Blissett

WILD WIND

'Whee-ee!' screamed the wild wind. 'Now for some fun.'
He blew the clouds faster and made them all run;
He snatched a balloon from a small boy's hand,
And whirled it and twirled it away from the land;
He raced round a house, bumped into a tree,
'Get out of my way, Sir!' he yelled angrily.
A dustbin lid clanked as it whisked away;
It rattled and rang as it joined in the play.
Then, rushing along, he saw a man's hat,
And he pulled it away, laughing, 'Man, catch that!'
He made all the aerials dance and shout,
And every umbrella he turned inside out;
Then, he decided he'd had enough play,
And with one last roar, he ran chuckling away.

Betty Tordoff

WHO I WOULD LIKE TO BE

To be Peter Pan,
To fly in the air,
Wouldn't it be great
To be up there.

To stop for an instance,
To be a child again inside,
Not to be an adult with
Feelings that we have to hide.

To be Thumbelina,
So, so small,
With the most beautiful
Singing voice of all.

Rapunzel, Rapunzel with
Her hair so long.
The prince was so handsome,
It's no wonder she was gone.

Snow White and Sleeping Beauty
And the wicked queens,
These are found in
Many of our dreams.

Fairies in the garden,
Toys that come alive,
Dungeons and dragons
And unicorns to ride.

To change into a mermaid,
Swimming in the sea,
There are so many characters
I would like to be.

Jackie Sutton

WORDS OF WISDOM

A little witch must always be
Pure in heart and honestly
Cast her spells to do much good
And bring such help to all who would

Consult her for her magic art
To bless their lives then merry part
And by this kind act all will be
Returned to her by power of three

But cast a spell to do some harm
A little witch would well be warned
This, too, returns by power of three
Creating witchy misery

So do the very best you can
To help your needful fellow man
Use your witch's power well
And cast a very potent spell!

Gail McClory

Boy In Bed Before Sleep

I - and my mate - don't believe in fairies -
I - and my pal - don't believe in elves -
Disbelief never varies
'Cos we listen to ourselves:
For what might just persuade us
As we sprint from day to day
Is that magic is never ominous
Whenever elves or fairies say,
'Let us help you!' -
But it is!

I - and my pal - don't believe in ghosties -
I - and my mate - don't believe in ghouls -
Disbelief never varies
'Cos we know that we're not fools:
For what might just persuade us
As we drift from night to day
Is that haunting is never dangerous
Whenever ghouls or ghosties say,
'Let us help you!' -
But it is!

When it's free we are beneath the sun,
In the wind and on grass beneath trees,
Then wily spirits know they've not won
'Cos life's stronger than death and us it frees!

But if I was always alone -
What might I believe in then?

S V Batten

VISITING GRANDMA

Grandma screamed
A mouse, a mouse
She jumped up on a chair
How we laughed
How we cried
To see her standing there.

She tore her hair
She stamped her feet
She looked around with fear
Just you watch
Just you wait
She yelled into my ear.

We joined the hunt
Around the house
But nowhere could we find
A little tail
Or whisker
No sign of any kind.

No mouse about
Now down you come
We pleaded but in vain
Out it shot
Across the floor
Dodged Grandpa's trusty cane.

The cat strode in
A hero bold
To do what must be done
Eyes steady
Paws ready
At last the mouse had gone.

Doreen Isherwood

WINNING WISDOM

'Why do you do such silly things,
Flapping your arms like bird wings?'
I said, 'Why do you
Not flap too?
You could even fly
Like a bird if you try.'
He didn't dare,
I didn't care.

'Why do you wear that funny hat?
You look stupid wearing that.'
I said, 'Why do you
Not wear one too?
Your head looks bare
With shaved-off hair.'
He said, 'No way!'
I went to play.

'Why is your face coloured all brown?
Is it the same all the way down?'
I said, 'Why are you
Not brown too?
Why do you think,
You are coloured pink?'
He didn't know,
I turned to go.

But he said, 'Let's pretend
We're flying, and lend
              me your hat.'
So now he's my friend
And that was the end
                of that.

Janet Forrest

THAT BOY?

Off we go to a land of dreams
Pursuing Harry through deadly schemes
Grabbing frogs, enhancing time
Precariously piloting to the sublime

Seeking the snitch, succeeding at will
Quiditch invariably a game of skill
In castle grounds of magic circles
Ducking and diving in feats of miracles

Watch out for the bludgers I hear you say
As Harry survives another day
His broomstick special a Nymbus 2000
He earned by conquering graphics commanded

Off to the dungeons, where soldiers hide
Armour clanging it's dark - no guide
Zapping away with his magic wand
Seeking friends - is this really fun?

Confronting live chess sets, intent to destroy
Little wizards - each girl or boy
But Harry's sorcery, sees him through
With the help of Hermione, she's really cool

In the garden of exploding snails
In search of Hagrid - an obscure trail
Levitating objects, obstructing doors
It's fun. It's excitement you're never bored

It's class it's cool a laugh for sure
Go on try it for it will cure
Stress, boredom, and depression
Here I go for another session

Audrey Polkinghorn

MOUSE HOUSE

I saw a small mouse
At the door of his house
Just a hole,
In the trunk of a tree.
Inside, it was warm
Whether rain, or wild storm
Quite tiny,
And not easy to see.
So be sure, that you
If you pass that way too
Remember,
To tread softly, and that,
Mouse house, may be near
So please keep your feet clear
Or you might
Squash the little mouse flat!

Patricia Whittle

FOOTBALL

It is *not* allowed in the hall
or indoors at all.
Neither upstairs *or* down
See them frown!

Not one smile
even when I'm quiet
for a little while -
    . . . until . . .
        I start to play again.

Aunt Jane loves me more than most
I play the host
when she comes to tea
even though I know
there may not be
a *single* cream cake for me.

Kinsman Clive

BAD BOY

There's a monster in the cupboard
At the bottom of the stairs.
If I walk close to the banister
I can hear it saying its prayers.

It eats small boys, who are naughty,
But if I tread softly on every stair
And miss the one that creaks loudly,
Perhaps it won't know that I'm there!

If I brush my teeth very loudly
And say nice things to my sister Clare.
Maybe it will think I'm a good boy
And won't drag me away to its lair.

Daddy thinks my ideas are useless.
'Monsters,' he says, 'are very wise
And not to be fooled by small naughty boys
Who spend most of their time telling lies.'

So, I think I will have to be better
And, at least sometimes, do as I'm told
Or I could try saying very loudly -
'That boy, he's 'as good as gold!''

Joyce M Jones

STRESSED OUT SPIDER

I live under the gutter
Not much of a life,
Hanging by my threat
Causes me some strife.
When the breeze comes
I swing about
And bang my head
It's such a stressful way to live
I'm sure I'd be better off dead!

D H Slape

HARRY WHO!

Harry Who! Is such a fool!
He thinks he's tough . . . and really cool

He spikes his hair like Gareth Gates
And tries to sing . . . to all his mates.

Friends, they laugh, at his antics,
But to me! He looks quite frantic.

Who is Harry? I'm not quite sure.
His surname now . . . let me think . . . is it Poor?

No wait . . . it's Flipper, no it's Floper?
I've got it now . . . his name is Potter!

Who? Harry Potter . . . never heard of him!

Sylvia Connor

THE MAGIC STONE

There was a boy called Neil
Who loved exploring caves,
One of which did then reveal -
A golden-headed maid.

Her name was Caracina,
Who dwelt in the cave of pearl.
She hoped that Neil could save her
For such horrors did occur.

A witch of deadly danger,
Did cast such ghastly deeds.
You'd hear her peels of laughter -
Above the salty - seas.

That stone you found above the rocks
Could help us with our work.
You see - it could do wondrous tricks,
We'll wait until it's dark.

Many of our mermen -
She changes into frogs,
Then locks them in a dungeon
To be eaten by the dogs.'

Devils - bats and demons,
Dragons - snakes or gnomes
Are lured into her mansion
To be cast in iron - chains.

'So if you rub the magic - stone
It'll break the witch's spell.'
Neil agreed and then went home
But no one did he tell.

Wendy Watkin